W9-ATB-357

EYE TWISTERS

BOGGLE, BAFFLE, AND BLOW YOUR MIND!

This edition published by Scholastic Inc., 557 Broadway, New York, NY 10012, by arrangement with Carlton Books Limited.

Scholastic and associated logos are trademarks or registered trademarks of Scholastic Inc.

Distributed by Scholastic Canada Ltd., Markham, Ontario
Scholastic Australia Pty. Ltd, Gosford NSW
Scholastic New Zealand Ltd., Greenmount, Auckland
Scholastic UK, Coventry, Warwickshire

Text, design and illustration copyright
© 2014 Carlton Books Limited

Author and Editor: Anna Bowles
Jacket Designer: Jake da'Costa
Designer: Rebecca Wright
Production: Ena Matagic

10 9 8 7 6 5 4 3 2 1

A catalogue record for this book is available from the British Library.

ISBN: 978-0-545-67843-8
Printed in Dongguan, China

EYE TWISTERS

BOGGLE, BAFFLE, AND BLOW YOUR MIND!

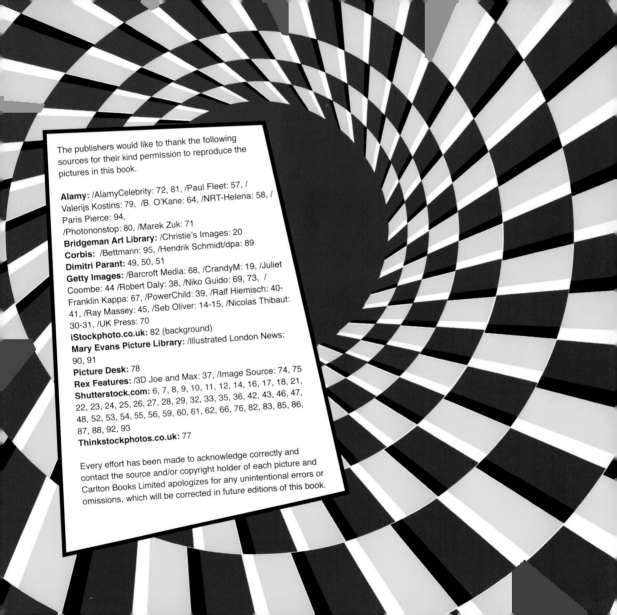

The publishers would like to thank the following sources for their kind permission to reproduce the pictures in this book.

Alamy: /AlamyCelebrity: 72, 81, /Paul Fleet: 57, / Valerijs Kostins: 79, /B. O'Kane: 64, /NRT-Helena: 58, / Paris Pierce: 94, /Photononstop: 80, /Marek Zuk: 71
Bridgeman Art Library: /Christie's Images: 20
Corbis: /Bettmann: 95, /Hendrik Schmidt/dpa: 89
Dimitri Parant: 49, 50, 51
Getty Images: /Barcroft Media: 68, /CrandyM: 19, /Juliet Coombe: 44 /Robert Daly: 38, /Niko Guido: 69, 73, / Franklin Kappa: 67, /PowerChild: 39, /Ralf Hiemisch: 40-41, /Ray Massey: 45, /Seb Oliver: 14-15, /Nicolas Thibaut: 30-31, /UK Press: 70
iStockphoto.co.uk: 82 (background)
Mary Evans Picture Library: /Illustrated London News: 90, 91
Picture Desk: 78
Rex Features: /3D Joe and Max: 37, /Image Source: 74, 75
Shutterstock.com: 6, 7, 8, 9, 10, 11, 12, 14, 16, 17, 18, 21, 22, 23, 24, 25, 26, 27, 28, 29, 32, 33, 35, 36, 42, 43, 46, 47, 48, 52, 53, 54, 55, 56, 59, 60, 61, 62, 66, 76, 82, 83, 85, 86, 87, 88, 92, 93
Thinkstockphotos.co.uk: 77

Every effort has been made to acknowledge correctly and contact the source and/or copyright holder of each picture and Carlton Books Limited apologizes for any unintentional errors or omissions, which will be corrected in future editions of this book.

OPTICAL ILLUSIONS...

What you see is not quite what you get! This book is full of pulsing patterns, twisting twirls, and impossible shapes that will bend your eyes upside out and downside in, leaving you feeling thoroughly boggled. There are also some tricks for you to try at home.

Enjoy and don't forget to blink!

Warning: some of the optical illusions in this book may cause dizziness or possibly epileptic seizures. If you start feeling dizzy or light-headed when viewing any of the images please look away.

IMPOSSIBLE CUBE

Drawing an object in three dimensions may seem impossible. Can you draw a cube like this one?

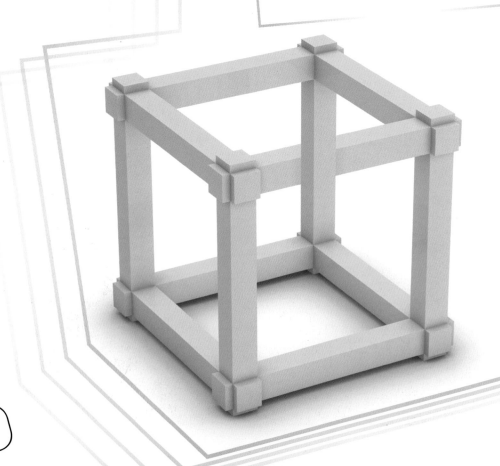

SCINTILLATING GRID

Look for the dots—but not too
hard, or they'll vanish!

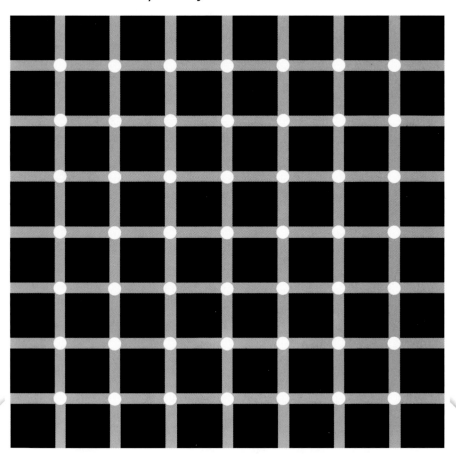

INTERLOCKING IMPOSSIBILITIES

Have the cubes from page 6 been multiplying?

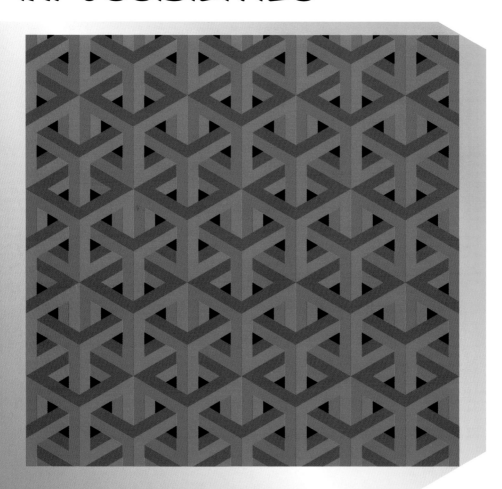

PULSATING PURPLE

Is this a crumpled napkin, or pulsating waves of color?

CONVEX OR CONCAVE?

Are you looking at the top of a pyramid, or peering down a tunnel?

CORNER QUANDARY

Are these cubes bulging out at you, or bending in? Can they do both?

BOGUS BULGE

The gradually changing shapes mimic a flat piece of paper that bulges. So a bulge is what you see!

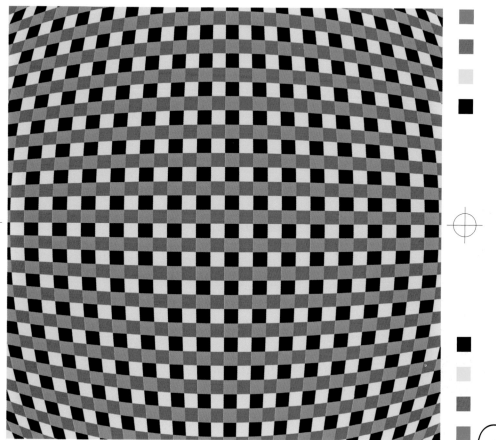

TRY THIS ONE AT HOME!

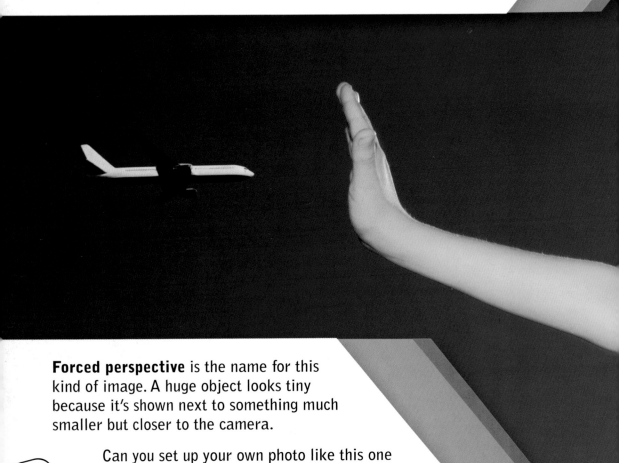

Forced perspective is the name for this kind of image. A huge object looks tiny because it's shown next to something much smaller but closer to the camera.

Can you set up your own photo like this one in your backyard or school playground?

ETERNAL TURNING

The wheels spin slowly and endlessly, until you look directly at one of them. Then, that one stops!

GIRLS OR GLASS?

In this classic illusion, do you see a fancy glass, or two faces?

TWITCHING TREE

Are the leaves hanging motionless on a hot day, or waving in a cool breeze?

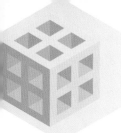

WHICH WINDOWS?

This is a very strange apartment building. Are those windows, skylights, or holes in the floor?

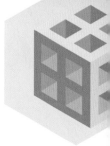

FRUIT FOOL?

This is an ordinary picture of a fruit basket ... until you turn it upside-down.

INWARD OR OUTWARD?

Multiple waterfalls of chocolate sliding into infinity, or a mud pie explosion. Which is it?

SPOT THE PETAL

Can you see petal shapes in this amazing image? Or are there just black and white squares?

COUNT THE CUBES

Can you pick out seven or more big cubes in this picture? Some of them are only partially visible.

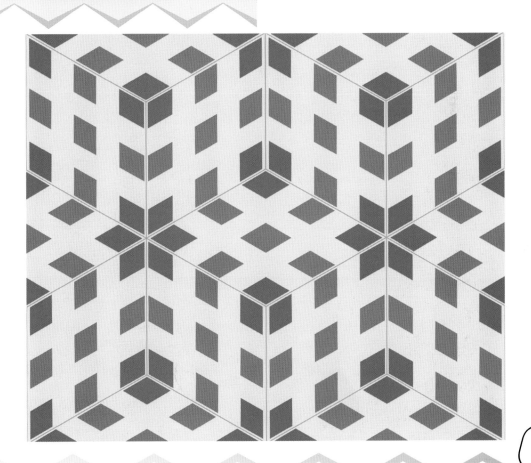

SEEING STARS

Stare at this circling illusion. The outer stars turn clockwise while the inner ones go the other way!

DICING WITH DIMENSIONS

This cube of dice is a more complex version of the illusion on page 8. Can you draw this one too?

SQUARING THE CIRCLE

Are these squares and rectangles flat or domed?

FLOWER BURSTS

Sit back and watch the flowers
grow before your eyes!

STATIONARY SHUFFLE

It's the dancers from page 10 again. Are they resting, or wriggling back and forth?

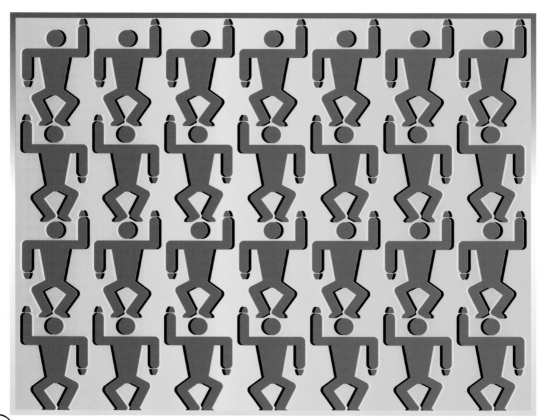

TRY THIS ONE AT HOME!

You don't need to visit the Leaning Tower of Pisa in Italy to set up a picture like this. Try it with a large tree.

STREET SEEN?

Can you spot which parts of this streetscape are real, and which are painted on a blank wall?

SUN SHOCK

The waves coming out of the sun seem to jerk in and out. Your eye expects to see one thing but actually sees another and quickly adjusts.

LINE UP THE LINES

Are the lines between the squares straight or do they bend? Your ruler may disagree with your eyes!

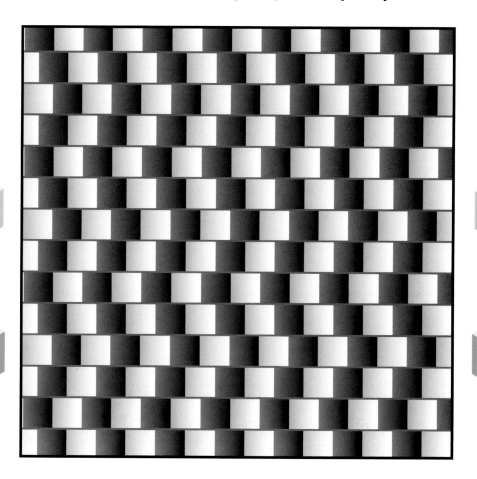

SKY TEASER

Can you guess what this is?
The answer is below.

TWO WAYS AT ONCE

This circling image seems to move in jerks.
Is the motion clockwise or counterclockwise?

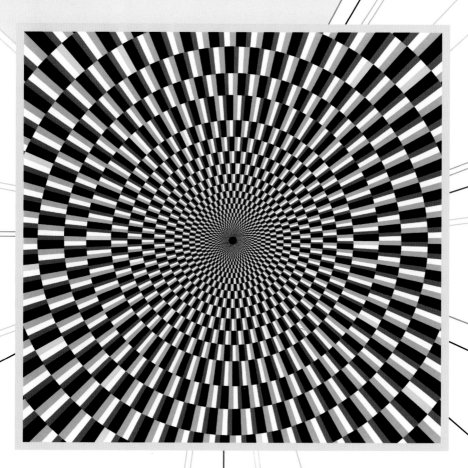

CHECKERBOARD WARP

Can you follow an alternating series of black and white squares from one side of the page to the other without blinking?

FLOORED!

This clever painting makes it look like there is a hole in the floor that goes through to a room below.

TRY THIS ONE AT HOME!

Here's another one you can do yourself. Get a friend to stand far away from you. Then hold up your hand and take a picture.

RHOMBUSES, REALLY

It's easy to see three-dimensional cubes here, but can you see two-dimensional rhombuses? (A rhombus has four sides of equal length and four angles that are not always right angles. One of them is outlined in black at the right.)

Rhombus

RAINBOW RAYS

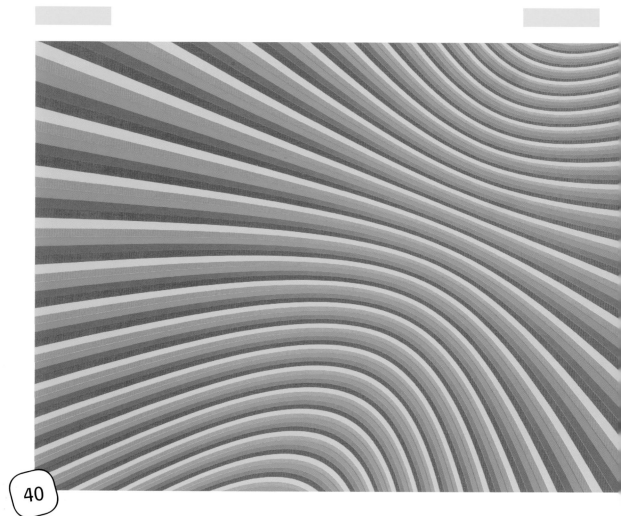

Are these lines bending inward or outward? When you stare at the
point where they bend, can you see a shimmering effect?

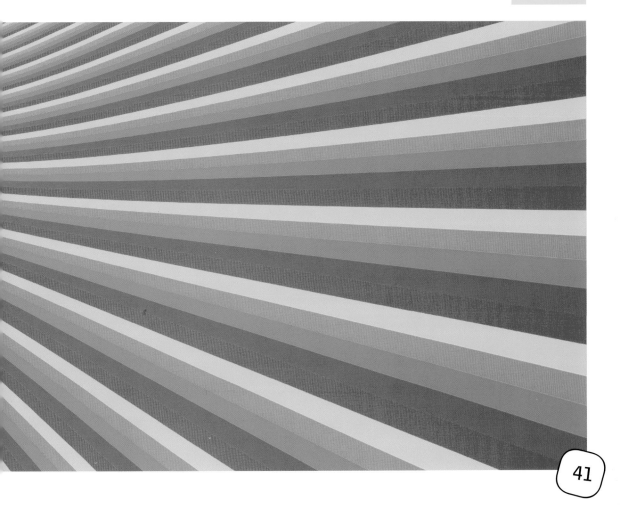

CRACKED?

Your brain thinks it knows what a building looks like, so it tries to correct your eyes even though they see the construction is impossible.

WHEELS WITHIN WHEELS

How many different circles of movement can you see at once?
Usually just the outer two circles seem to move, but can you
see the inner ones moving?

WINDOW OR WHAT?

You've probably guessed this isn't a real window. But what is it? The answer is below.

It's a sundial.

MERGED ZEES

Do you see a light gray forward Z
or a black backward one?

TWISTING TEST

How long can you stare at the spinning circle without blinking? Time yourself!

BALANCING ACT

These acrobats are performing on an impossible shape. Who do you think will fall off first?

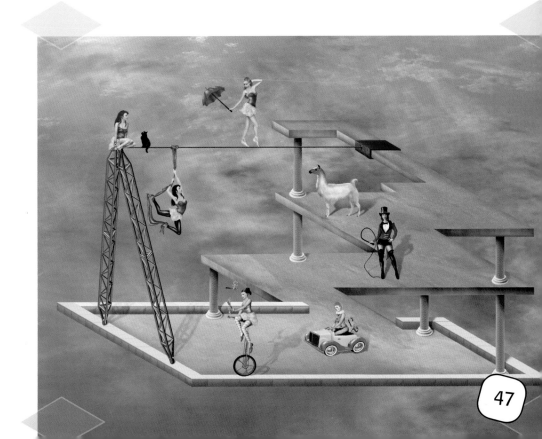

MANGLED MECHANISM

Not only would these wheels never turn in real life,
but you could never build them in the first place.

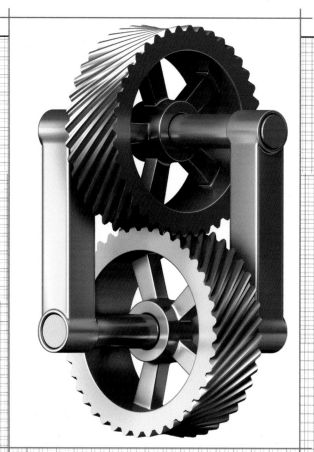

AFTERIMAGES

Stare at the big dot in the middle of the girl's forehead for 30 seconds. Then close your eyes. What do you see?

These afterimage portraits by Dimitri Parant
work by overstimulating some cells in the eye
and understimulating others.

LASER LIGHTS

This moving illusion consists of the pattern made by a reflected laser beam.

WINK AT ME

If you look at this illusion with one eye instead of both, it may move less or not at all. Your brain is receiving less opposite information with only one eye open.

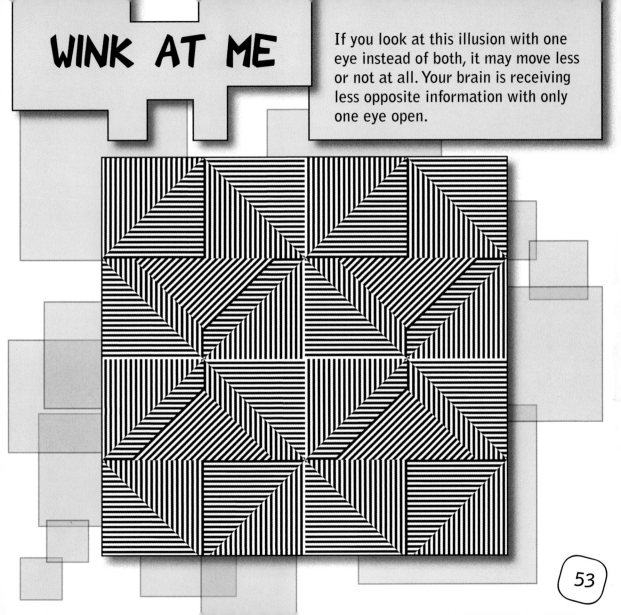

SIDE STREET

This building in Spain invites you to stroll … through a brick wall!

ETERNITY RING

This simple illusion has no beginning and no end,
but it looks as if you could wear it on your finger.

SPINNING TUNNEL

The Vs seem to circle endlessly. But do the ones on the red streak seem to move less than the others?

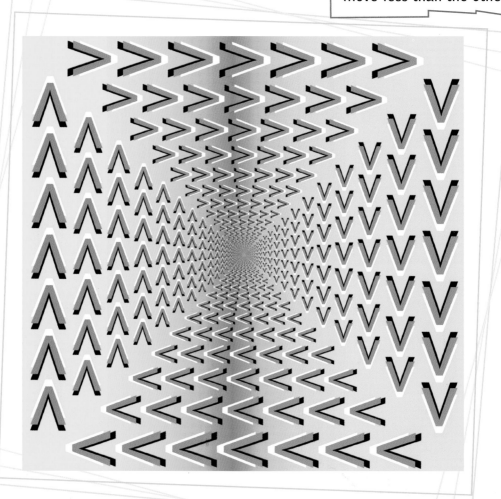

PENGUIN PLAYGROUND

Is the water flowing up or down in this image?

PLUMBING THE HEIGHTS

This is not actually an optical illusion, but a real sculpture in Ypres, Belgium.

BURSTING BULGE

This illusion is a more protruding version of the Bogus Bulge on page 13.

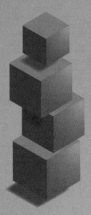

CUBE ACCUMULATION

In this kind of image, each cube looks entirely realistic on its own. But they add up to something much less likely.

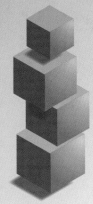

WHO ARE WE?

The princess and her grumpy stepmother ... or the other way around?

Hint: The princess' bangs turn into the stepmother's nose!

TRY THIS ONE AT HOME!

You might not have a birdbath the size of the one outside this Bavarian castle, but try holding a dish in front of your house so that the house "sits" on it.

ELECTRIC AVENUE

If you stand in the right place, this piece of street art in Poland looks three-dimensional.

STRETCHING CREDIBILITY

This sculpture in Cairo, Egypt, is possible because the "rocks" are made of a light material like papier-mâché. It looks like the top rock is floating, although it is held up by the solid "rope."

OLD OR YOUNG?

This optical illusion was printed on a German postcard in 1888. It can be seen either as a young girl from the back, or an old woman looking to the left.

CALM CENTER?

By focusing on the yellow dot in the center, can you make this pulsing image stay still?

If you removed two cubes from this figure, it would cease to be an illusion. Can you work out which ones they are?

The two that form a bar across the middle of the figure.

THAT'S CRAZY!

A cyclist comes face to face with jungle street art created by Kurt Wenner.

TRY THIS ONE AT HOME!

You could be a giant! Stand close to the camera. Have your friend stand farther away until it looks like you're about to crush him. Then, let him have a turn at being a giant.

HANGING AROUND

Artist Leandro Erlich set up a housefront on the ground and hung a huge mirror above it so people could lie down and see themselves "suspended" from the walls!

PORT CUT

Did this homeowner chop through her wall
to provide quick access to the beach?

SEWER SURPRISE

Take a look inside a fake sewer in this street art by 3D Joe and Max.

TRY THIS ONE AT HOME!

Set up this shot in your local park. You'll need three friends. One of you stand close to the camera. Have another friend stand back farther. The last person will tell everyone how to adjust and take the photo.

Use a smartphone or camera to take a picture of a part of your face, and then hold it in front of the same part of someone else's face for a funny switch!

75

SQUIRMING CIRCLE

Can you count the Vs in the center circle, or do they squirm too much? The total is below.

There are 59 Vs in the center circle.

SUSPENSION OF DISBELIEF

The "natural" way the light is shown here fools the eye into thinking this image should work like a real shelf.

SHIFTING SANDS

Do you see a desert scene, a dog, or a face? Or all three?

PULSATING BLACK HOLE

The blue lozenges rush to be swallowed up, but never actually get there.

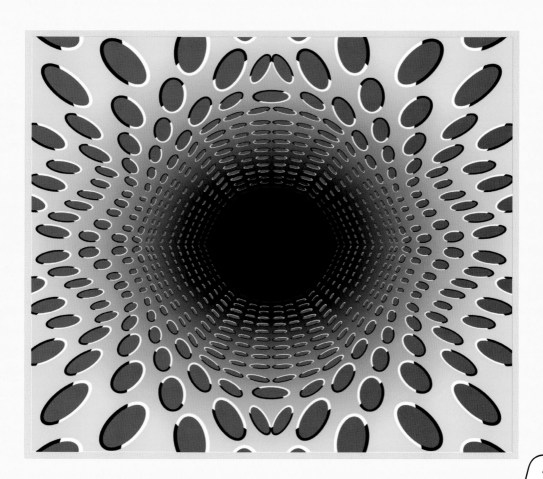

TRY THIS ONE AT HOME!

Shrink a tall person down to size! Stand closer to the camera than the tall person while you have your picture taken. Try it in front of water!

ROYAL VIEW

This amazing art is drawn on a flat surface but looks like a bird's eye view of William and Kate's Royal Wedding in 2011.

MARVELOUS MARBLE

The biggest marble spins without needing to be pushed!

WATER BOGGLER

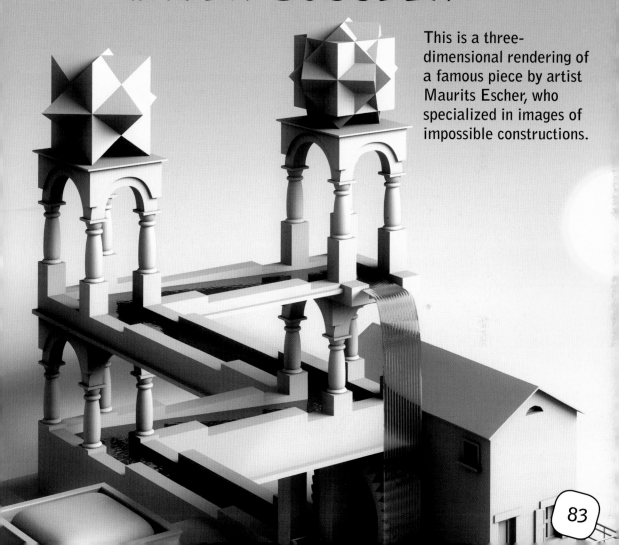

This is a three-dimensional rendering of a famous piece by artist Maurits Escher, who specialized in images of impossible constructions.

THE BIG CITY

A model city? No, this is a real suburb of Istanbul, Turkey captured with tilt-shift photography, which creates a blur around the edge of an image and sharpens the center.

ENDLESS CLIMB

Can you make this impossible staircase out of paper?
Cut out a square with a hole inside and make the steps
separately, then glue them together.

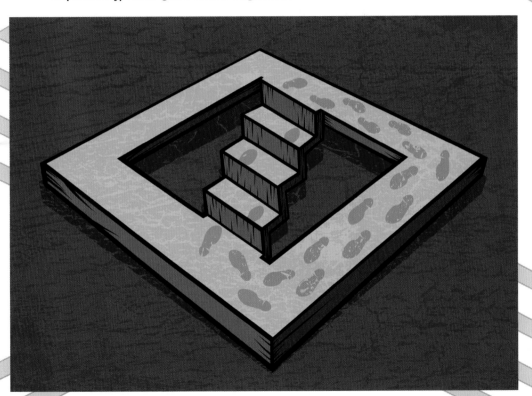

MAGIC MOSAIC

This two-dimensional image seems to move like the beads in a kaleidoscope.

THE PARROWDOX

Copy this drawing. First, draw the lines. Then, add the shading. The shading adds to the three-dimensional look.

UNDULATING PAPER

This illusion uses the bulge effect seen on pages 13 and 59 to create an effect of multiple waves.

BREAKING BOUNDS

Because we are so used to seeing pictures within frames, a picture that spills over looks like a real object. Here the tiger, the frame, and the shadow are all painted.

GHOST IMAGES

These negatives of Clark Gable and Greta Garbo work similarly to the afterimages on pages 49 to 51. Stare at the four white dots for 30 seconds, then shut your eyes.

ARROW WRAP

Is the green arrow bent or straight?

TRY THIS ONE AT HOME!

Face a large mirror. The two mirrors opposite one another will create a never-ending reflection.

FIND THE RABBIT

Can you find the head of a rabbit in this old illustration of a hawk? The answer is below.

It's on the front edge of the wing nearest to us.

DOWNSIDE UP?

Is this a man with a beard and strange hair ... or a man with a beard and strange hair?

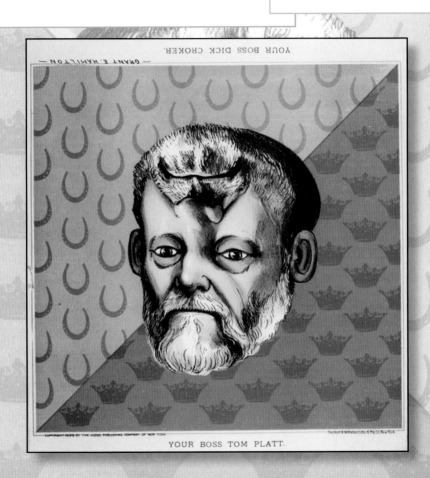